# ANTHOLOGY OF CLASSICS

# CONTENTS

# OVER MY HEAD

Words and Music by
CHRISTINE McVIE

oh, but it sure
D
G/D
D
feels nice.
You can take me an - y time you like.
G/D
D
I'll be a - round if you think

Em
you might
love
me, ba - by,
D
and hold me tight.
G/D
D
D
G
Your mood is like a cir - cus wheel.
D
G

D
G
x000
You're chang - ing all the time.
Some - times I can't help but feel that I'm
3
wast - ing all of my time.
A
G/D
I think I'm look - ing on the dark side.

G/D
D
But ev-'ry day,
you hurt my pride.
I'm o-ver my
Em
head,
oh,
but it
D
G/D
D
Repeat and fade
Em
sure feels nice.
D
G/D
D

# SAY YOU LOVE ME

Words and Music by
CHRISTINE McVIE

A
er.
I'm tin-gling right
I'm beg-ging you
I guess I'm not
from my head to my toes.
for a lit-tle sym-pa-thy.
as strong as I used to be.
So
And if you
And if you
E A/E D/E E A
help me, help me, help me make the feel-ing go.
use me a-gain, it-'ll be the end of me.
use me a-gain, it-'ll be the end of me.
D/F♯ E F♯m E D A
'Cause when the lov-ing starts and the lights go down and

F♯m
E
A
there's not an-oth-er liv-ing soul a-round, you woo me un-til the sun
D
comes up. And you say that you love me.
1.
Have
2.
3.
Say that you love me.
Repeat and fade
Fall-in', fall-in', fall-in'.

# LITTLE LIES

Words and Music by
CHRISTINE McVIE and EDDIE QUINTELA

F♯m7/E
D
E/D
Dmaj7
E/D
re - ar - range just a day or two. (Close my, close
un - der - stand there's a rea - son why. (Close your, close
Dmaj7
E/D
A
F♯m
my, close my eyes.) But, I could - n't find
your, close your eyes.) No more bro -
F♯m
F♯m7/E
a way, so, I'll set - tle for one day to be -
ken hearts. we're bet - ter off a - part, let's give

D
E/D
Dmaj7
E/D
Dmaj7
E/D
lieve in you.
it a try.
(Tell me, tell me, tell me
A
F♯m
A 6/9
A
lies.)
Tell me lies, tell me sweet lit - tle lies.
D
F♯m7/E
F♯m
(Tell me lies.)
(Tell me, tell me lies.)
Oh no, no you

A6/9
A
D
F♯m7(addB)/E
To Coda
can't dis - guise.
(You can't dis - guise.
(No you can't dis - guise.)
F♯m
A6/9
A
D
Tell me lies, tell me sweet lit - tle lies.
F♯m7/E
Dmaj7
E
Dmaj7
E
Dmaj7
E
Dmaj7
E
Dmaj7
E

D.S. 𝄋 al Coda ⊕
47
Dmaj7
E
Dmaj7
E
Dmaj7
Dmaj7/E
Repeat and fade
Coda
F♯m
A6/9
A
Tell me lies, tell me sweet lit - tle lies.
D
F♯m7/E
F♯m
(Tell me lies.)
(Tell me, tell me lies.)
Oh no, no you
A6/9
A
D
F♯m7(addB)
E
can't dis - guise.
(You can't dis - guise.)
(No you can't dis - guise.)

# TUSK

Words and Music by
LINDSEY BUCKINGHAM

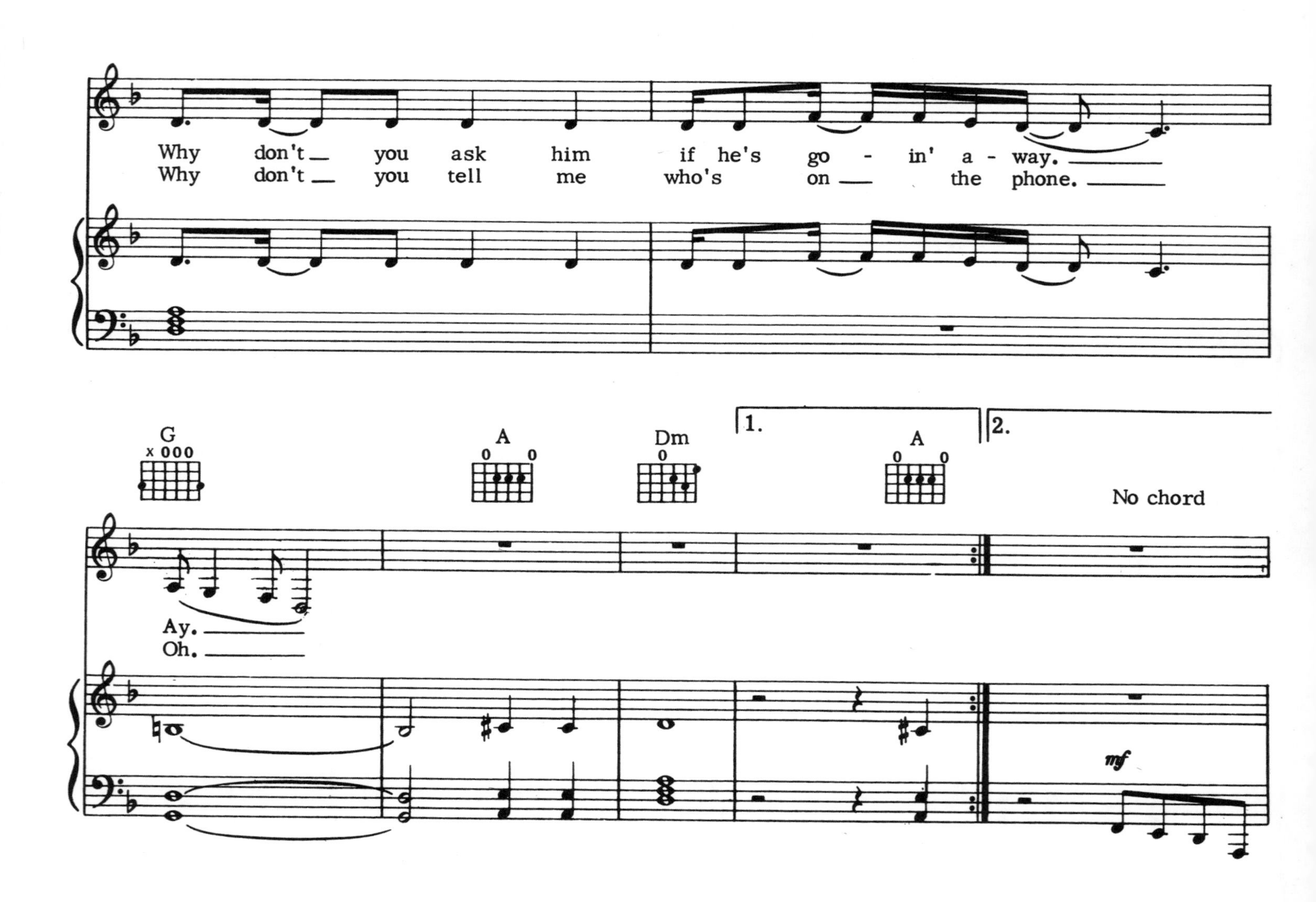

Dm(no3rd)
Dm(no3rd)
Why don't you ask him what's go - in' on.
Why don't you ask him the lat-est on his throne.
Oh,

G(no3rd)
A(no3rd)
oh,
oh.
Don't say that you
Dm
love me.
C
G
C
A
Just tell me that you
Dm
want me.

C
G
C
A
Tusk!
Just say that you
Dm
want me.
C
G
C
A
Repeat and fade
Dm
Tacet
Don't tell me that you...
C
G
C
A
Tusk!

# GO YOUR OWN WAY

Words and Music by
LINDSEY BUCKINGHAM

Bb
F
How can I when you won't take it from me?
O-pen up. Ev-'ry-thing's wait-ing for you.
Dm
Bb
C
Dm
You can go your own way, go your own way. You can call
Bb
C
Dm
it an-oth-er lone-ly day. You can go
Bb
C
1.
2.
D. S. and fade
your own way, go your own way. your own way.

# RHIANNON

Words and Music by
STEVIE NICKS

F
bird in flight. And who will be her lov - er?
fine sky - lark and when the sky is star - less.
C
All your life, you've nev - er seen a wom-an
F
tak - en by the
wind.
C
Would you stay if she prom - ised you heav-en?
F
Will you ev - er
1.
win?
2.
win?

Am
Will you ev - er win?
F
Am
Rhi - an - non.
F
Am
Rhi - an - non.
F
Tak - en by, tak - en by the sky.

Am
F
Tak - en by, tak -
en by the sky.
Am
F
Repeat and fade
Am
Dreams un - wind. Love's
a state of mind.
F

# AS LONG AS YOU FOLLOW

Words and Music by
CHRISTINE McVIE
and EDDY QUINTELA

you find at the end of a rain -
was rough to get back where you
Dm
F
bow.
I've been dream - in'
are.
And the sun went down,
B♭
though it was in vain.
Ah, but now
nev - er seemed to rise.
Ah, but now
C
you're here; can't be - lieve that you're back a - gain.
you're here with the light shin - ing in your eyes.

Chorus:
Dm
Now I know I can't lose
F
Dm
as long as you fol - low.
B♭
C
F
I'm gon - na win,
I'm gon - na beg, steal or bor -
1.
Dm
B♭
C
row
as long as you fol - low.

Dm
D.S. 𝄋
2. 3. Dm
I've _ been
row. _
B♭
C
F
Yes, I _ can live to - day
if you give _ me to - mor -
Dm
Last time To Coda
B♭
C
Dm
- row, _
as long as you fol - low. _
B♭
A

Dm
C
G/B
G
F/C
C7
F/C
C7
F/C
C11
8fr.
D.S.S. al Coda
Now I know I can't lose,
Coda
Bb
C
long as you fol - low;
Repeat and fade
F
Dm
Bb
C
as long as you fol - low;

# EVERYWHERE

Words and Music by
CHRISTINE McVIE

F
C
Dm7
B♭
C
Dm7
You know_ that I'm proud and I can't get the words out._ Oh,
You bet-ter make it soon be-fore you break_ my heart._ Oh,
I,
B♭
C
Dm7
C
B♭
C
I want to be with you ev - 'ry - where._ Oh,
Dm7
B♭
C
Dm7
C
To Coda
I,
I want to be with you ev -

1.
Bb
C
F
C
F
C
'ry - where, I wan-na be with you ev - 'ry - where.
F
C
Dm7
Bb
2.
Bb
C
'ry - where. I wan-na be with you ev -
Bb
C/Bb
Bb
C/Bb
Bb
C/Bb
Bbmaj7
C/Bb
'ry-where.
Bb
C/Bb
Bbmaj7
C/Bb
Bb
C/Bb
Bbmaj7
D.S. al Coda

Coda
Bb
C
C
Dm7
Bb
C
'ry - where._ Oh, I,
Dm7
C
Bb
C
Dm7
I want to be with you ev - 'ry - where._ Oh, I,
Bb
C
Dm7
C
Bb
C
I want to be with you ev - 'ry - where,_ I wan-na be with you ev -

3rd Verse

Can you hear me calling
out you name?
You know that I'm falling
and I don't know what to say.

Come along baby
We better make a start.
You better make it soon
before you break my heart.

# DREAMS

Words and Music by
STEVIE NICKS

F
G
x000
F
It's on - ly right
It's on - ly me
G
x000
F
G
x000
that you should play the way you feel it. But
who wants to wrap a - round your dreams. And
F
G
x000
F
lis - ten care - ful - ly to the sound of your lone-
have you an - y dreams you'd like to sell? Dreams of lone-
G
x000
F
G
x000
li - ness, like a heart - beat, drives you mad, in the still-
li - ness, like a heart - beat, drives you mad, in the still-

F
G
x000
F
ness of re-mem - ber - ing what you had
ness of re-mem - ber - ing what you had
G
x000
F
G
x000
and what you lost
and what you lost
and what you had
and what you had
F
G
x000
F
and what you lost.
and what you lost.
G
x000
Fmaj7
x 0
G6
x0000
Fmaj7
x 0
Oh, thun - der on - ly hap - pens when it's rain - ing.

G6
Fmaj7
G6
Play-ers on-ly love you when they're play-
Fmaj7
G6
Fmaj7
ing.
Say, wom-en, they will come
G6
Fmaj7
G6
and they will go.
Fmaj7
G6
Fmaj7
To Coda
When the rain wash-es you clean, you'll know.

G6
Fmaj7
G
You'll
know.
F
Am
G
F
D. S. al Coda
Coda
G6
Fmaj7
You'll
know.
G6
Fmaj7
G6
Fmaj7 (add B)
You will
know.
Oh,
you'll
know.

# YOU MAKE LOVIN' FUN

Words and Music by
CHRISTINE McVIE

Gm
3 fr.
Oh, can it be so?
You, you make lov-ing fun.
F
This feel - ing fol - lows me wher - ev - er I go.
And I don't have to tell you you're the on - ly
Eb
one.
To Coda
Bb
I nev-er did be - lieve
Bb/Ab
in mir - a - cles.
Gm7
3 fr.
F
But I've a feel-ing it's time to try.

Eb
Bb
I never did believe
Bb/Ab
in the ways of magic.
Gm7
3 fr.
But I'm be-
F
Eb
D. S. al Coda
ginning to wonder why.
Don't,
Coda
Repeat and fade
Bb
F
Eb
You, you make loving fun.
Repeat and fade

# SECOND HAND NEWS

Words and Music by
LINDSEY BUCKINGHAM

A D E
lay me down_ in the tall grass and let me do_ my stuff._
could - n't you_ just let me go down and do_ my stuff._
A D A
I know_ I got noth - in' on you._
I know_ you're hop - in' to find_
D A
I know_ there's noth - in'_ to do._ When times_
some - one_ who's gon - na give you_ peace of mind._ When times_
E7 A E7
_ go bad_ and you can't_ get_ e - nough,_ won't you
_ go bad,_ when times_ go_ rough,_ won't you

A
D
E
lay me down in the tall grass and let me do my stuff.
lay me down in the tall grass and let me do my stuff.
A
D
Scat sing
A
E
A
D

A
To Coda
1.
E
A
2.
E
A
D.S.
al Coda
Coda
E
A
Repeat and fade
A
Bm/A
A
Bm/A
I'm just sec - ond hand news, I'm just sec - ond hand news.
Repeat and fade
A
D
E

DON'T STOP

Words and Music by
CHRISTINE McVIE
Medium Rock beat
E A/E E A/E E A/E E A/E
mf
E D A E D
If you wake up and don't want to smile; if it takes just a
Why not think a-bout times to come, and not a-bout the
All I want is to see you smile, if it takes just a
A E D A
lit-tle while, o-pen your eyes and look at the day.
things that you've done. If your life was bad to you,
lit-tle while. I know you don't be-lieve that it's true.
B E D/E
You'll see things in a dif-f'rent way.
just think what to-mor-row will do.
I nev-er meant an-y harm to you.
Don't stop

A
E
D/E
A
thinking about tomorrow. Don't stop. It'll soon be here.
E
D/E
A
It'll be better than before.
B
1. 2.
3.
Yesterday's gone. Yesterday's gone. terday's gone.
Repeat and fade
E
D/E
A
E
D/E
A
Ooh, don't you look back.

# NEVER GOING BACK AGAIN

Words and Music by
LINDSEY BUCKINGHAM

G
D
G
let me in;
means to win.
D
G
D
G
D
G
made me see where I've been.
Come down and see me a - gain.
D
G
D
G
D

G
D
G
D
Been down one time.
G
D
G
Been down two times.
Em
Bm7
Em
D
G
D
I'm nev-er go-ing back a-gain.
G
D
G
D

To Coda
G
D
G
D
G
D
G
D
G
D
G
D
G
D
G
D
G
D
D. S. al Coda
Coda
G
Em
Bm7
Em
D
G
D
G

# HOLD ME

Words and Music by
CHRISTINE McVIE
and ROBBIE PATTON

Am7 G D G/D D G/D D
and me got plen - ty of time.
I'm the fool pay - in' the dues.
There's no - bod -
I'm just
Am7 G Am7 G D G/D D
y in the fu - ture, so ba - by, let me hand you my love.
a - round the cor - ner, if you got a min - ute to spare.
G/D D Am7 G Am7 G
There's no step for you to dance to, so slip your hand in - side my
I'll be wait - in' for you, if you ev - er wan - na be
D G/D D G/D D G Am7
glove.
there.
Hold me, hold

G/B
C
D
me,
hold
me.
G
Am7
G/B
C
D
hold
me,
Hold
me,
hold
me.
1.
2.
Repeat and fade
G
Am7
hold
I
Hold
me,
G/B
C
D
me,
hold
me.

# LOVE IN STORE

Words and Music by
CHRISTINE McVIE and JIM RECOR

C
F
In - stead of bring - in' me down.
I'm scared of feel - in' that way.
in - stead of bring - in' me down.
I'm scared of feel - in' that way.
I can't fight it an - y - more.
G/F
Fmaj7
G/F
Since you've been a - round,
we've got love in store.
1.
C
Dm/C
G7/C
C
Dm/C
G7/C
2.
C
Dm
G
Am
F
G
Nev - er take your love a - way.

C
Dm G Am F
Beg - gin' you, ba - by.
Nev - er take your love a - way.
G
C
Oh, dar - lin'.
Nev -
Dm G Am F G
er take your love a - way.
Repeat and fade
C
Dm/C G7/C
C
Dm/C G7/C

# TANGO IN THE NIGHT

Words and Music by
LINDSEY BUCKINGHAM

Am
Am/G
Try to sleep, sleep won't come,
In - side, out - side,
Am/F
just as I be-gin to fade.
no lone - li-ness in-side.
Am/G
Am5
Then I re - mem-ber,
f

G5
when the moon was full and bright.
I would take you in the dark - ness
F5
Am5
and do the tan - go in the night,
tan - go.
ff
G5
1. F5

2.
F5
Am
Bum, huh, huh, bum, bum, huh, huh, huh, huh, huh, huh, huh, huh. Bum,
p
bum, huh, huh, bum, bum, huh, huh, huh, huh, huh, huh, huh, huh. Bum, bum, huh, huh, bum, bum, huh, huh, huh,
Repeat and fade (Guitar solo ad lib)
Am
huh, huh, huh, huh, huh. Bum, bum, huh, huh, bum, bum.
f
G
F

# OH DADDY

Words and Music by
CHRISTINE McVIE

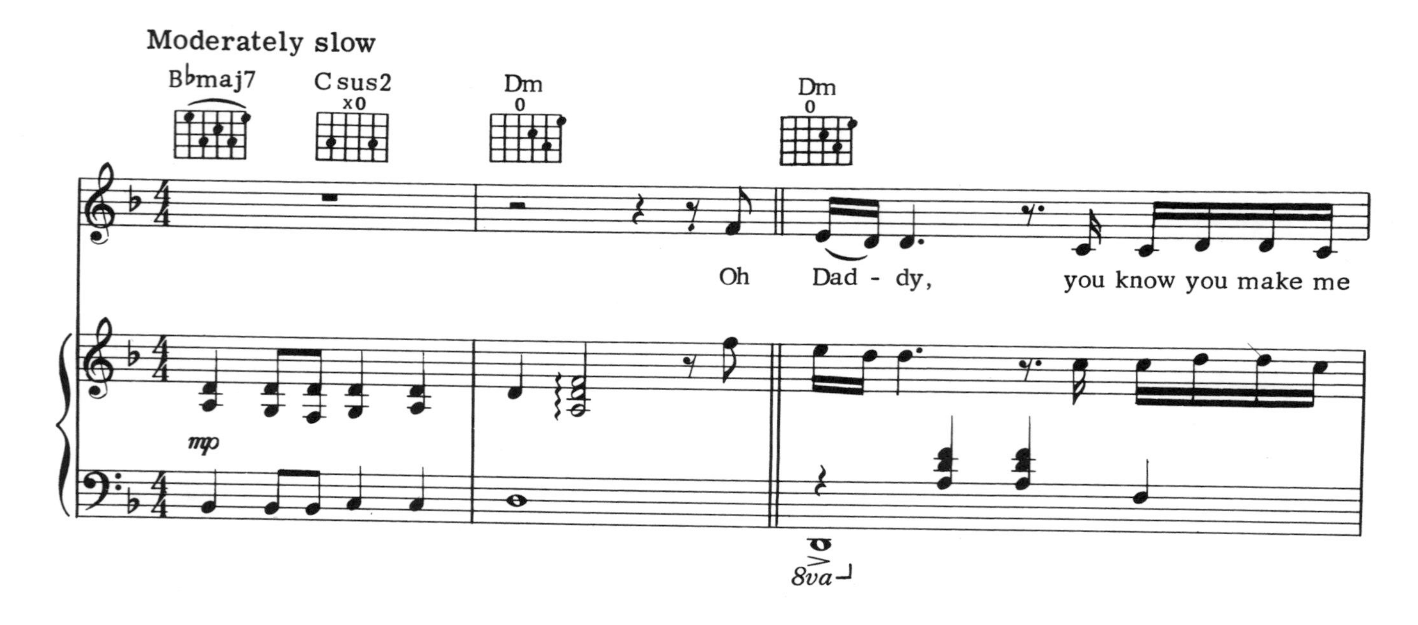


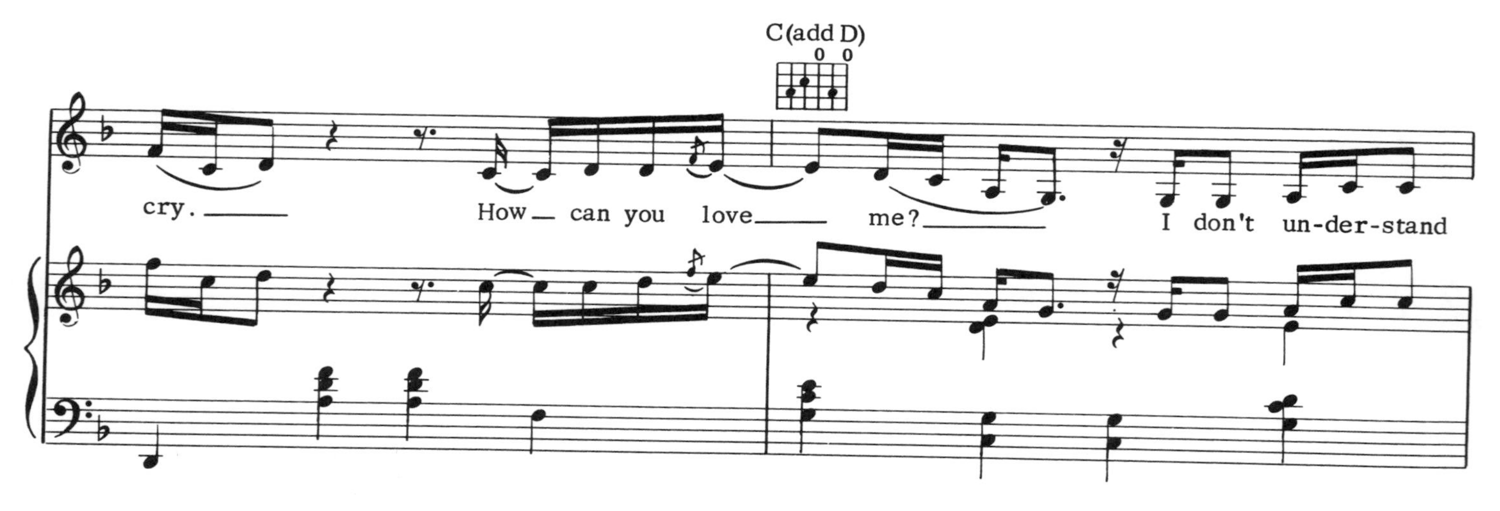


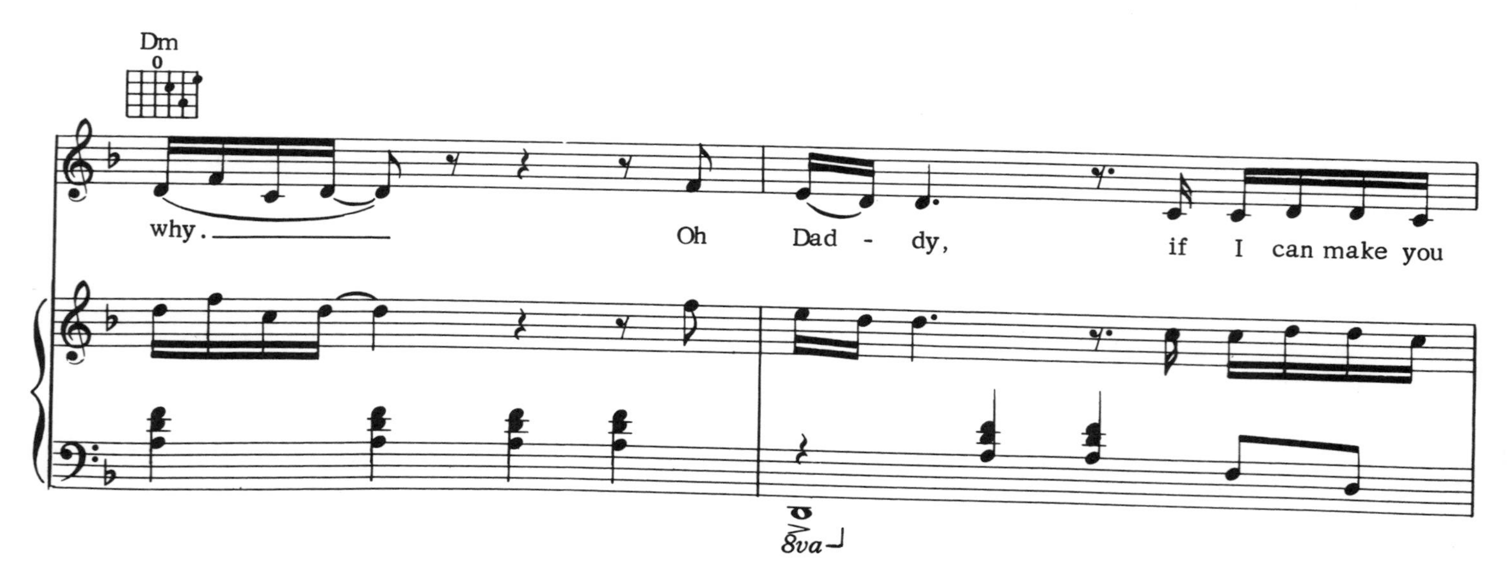

C(add D)
see, if there's been a fool a - round, it's got to be me.
Dm
Gm7
3 fr.
Am7
Dm
Yes, it's got to be me.
Oh
Dm
Dad - dy, you soothe me with your smile. You're let-ting me know
8va
loco
C
Dm
you're the best thing in my life.
Oh

Dad - dy, if I can make you see, if there's been a fool a-
8va loco
C
Dm
Gm7
3 fr.
Am7
To Coda
round, it's got to be me. Yes, it's got to be me.
Dm
B♭maj7
B♭/C
C7
Why are you right when I'm so wrong?
Dm
B♭maj7
B♭/C
C7
I'm so weak, but you're so strong.

Dm
Bbmaj7
Bb/C
C7
Ev - 'ry-thing you do is just all right.
Dm
Bbmaj7
And I can't walk a - way from you, ba - by, if I tried.
p
Dm
D. S. al Coda
Oh
Coda
Dm
Gm7
3 fr.
Am7
Yes, it's got to be me.
Dm
Gm7
3 fr.
Am7
Dm
Gm7
3fr.
Am7
Dm
Yes, it's got to be me.

# SARA

Words and Music by
STEVIE NICKS

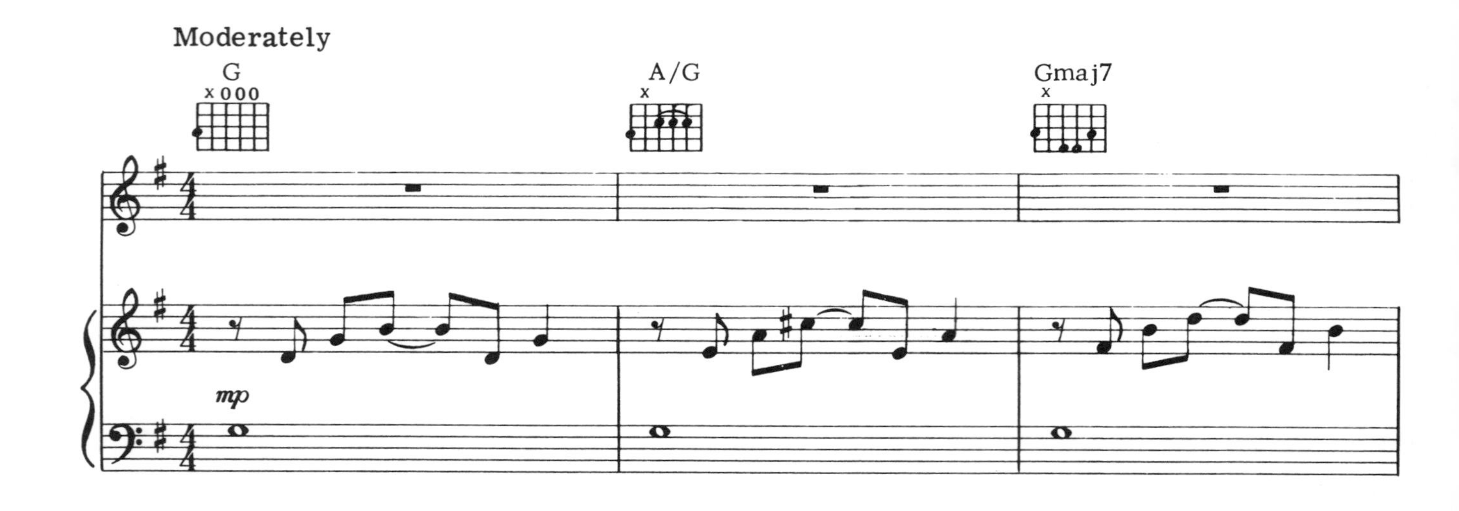


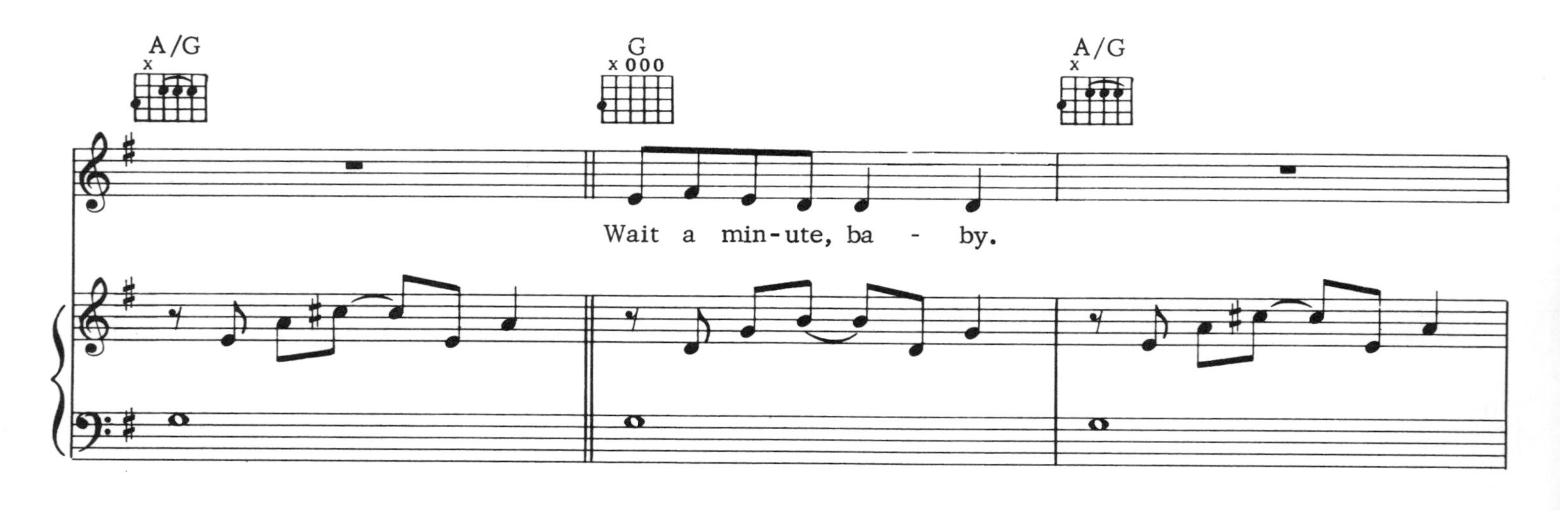

A/G
Gmaj7
A/G
but you nev - er told ___ me 'bout the fire. ___
G
A/G
Gmaj7
A/G
G
D/G
G
D/G
G
D/G
Em7
D/E
Em7
D/E
Em7
D/E
mf
G/C
D/C
G/C
D/C
G/C
D/C
G/D
D
G/D
D
G/D
D

G D/G G D/G G D/G Em7 D/E Em7 D/E Em7 D/E
Drown-in' in the sea of love_ where
G/C D/C G/C D/C G/C D/C G/D D G/D D G/D D
ev-'ry-one___ would love_ to drown. But
G D/G G D/G G D/G Em7 D/E Em7
now it's gone. It does-n't mat-ter what for.
D/E Em7 D/E G/C D/C G/C D/C G/C D/C
When you build_ your house,___ then

G/D
D
G/D
D
G/D
D
G
A/G
Gmaj7
call me home.
G
A/G
Gmaj7
G/A
A
Bm/A
G/A
A
Bm/A
G
A/G
Gmaj7
And he was just like a great dark
G
A/G
Gmaj7
G/A
A
Bm/A
wing with-in the wings of a storm.

G/A
A
Bm/A
G
A/G
Gmaj7
I think I had met my match.
He was sing-in'
and un - do - ing,
and un - do - ing

G/A
A
Bm/A
G
A/G
Gmaj7
the lac - es,
G
A/G
Gmaj7
G/A
A
Bm/A
un-do - ing the lac - es.
G/A
A
Bm/A
G
D/G
G
D/G
G
D/G
Em7
D/E
Em7
D/E
Em7
D/E
G/C
D/C
G/C
D/C
G/C
D/C

G/D D G/D D G/D D G D/G G D/G G D/G
Said, Sar - a, you're the
Em7 D/E Em7 D/E Em7 D/E G/C D/C G/C
po - et in my heart. Nev - er change.
D/C G/C D/C G/D D G/D D G/D D
Nev - er stop. But
G D/G G D/G G D/G Em7 D/E Em7
3
now it's gone. It does-n't mat - ter what for.

D/E
Em7
D/E
G/C
D/C
G/C
D/C
G/C
D/C
But when you build your house,
then
G/D
D
G/D
D
G/D
D
G
A/G
Gmaj7
call me home.
G
A/G
Gmaj7
G/A
A
Bm/A
G/A
A
Bm/A
G
A/G
Gmaj7
Hold on.
The night is

G
A/G
Gmaj7
G/A
A
Bm/A
coming. And the starling flew for days.
I'd stay home at night
all the time. I go anywhere,
anywhere, anywhere. Ask me, and

G
A/G
Gmaj7
I'm there.
Ask me, and
G/A
A
Bm/A
I'm there,
'cause I
care.
Repeat and fade
Em7
D/E
D/G
Sar - a.
G/C
D/C
G/D
D

# SONGBIRD

Words and Music by
CHRISTINE McVIE

F
the sun will be shin - in'.
I'll nev - er be cold,
And 'Cause I feel
Gm
3 fr.
B♭
Dm
B♭
that when I'm with you, it's al - right;
I know it's
F
right.
1.
To
2.
C
B♭
And the song - birds are keep sing - ing like they know the score.
cresc.
mf

Dm
Bb
And I love you, I love you, I love
decresc.
mp
C 11
F
To Coda
you like nev-er be-fore.
Bb
F
Bb
F
And I wish

Gm
3 fr.
Bb
Dm
Bb
you all the love in the world;
but
C 11
F
most of all, I wish it from my - self.
D. S. al Coda
And the song-
cresc.
Coda
C 11
F
Like nev-er be-fore.
C 11
F
C 11
F
Like nev-er be-fore.
rit.

# NO QUESTIONS ASKED

Words and Music by
STEVIE NICKS and KELLY JOHNSTON

Moderately fast rock

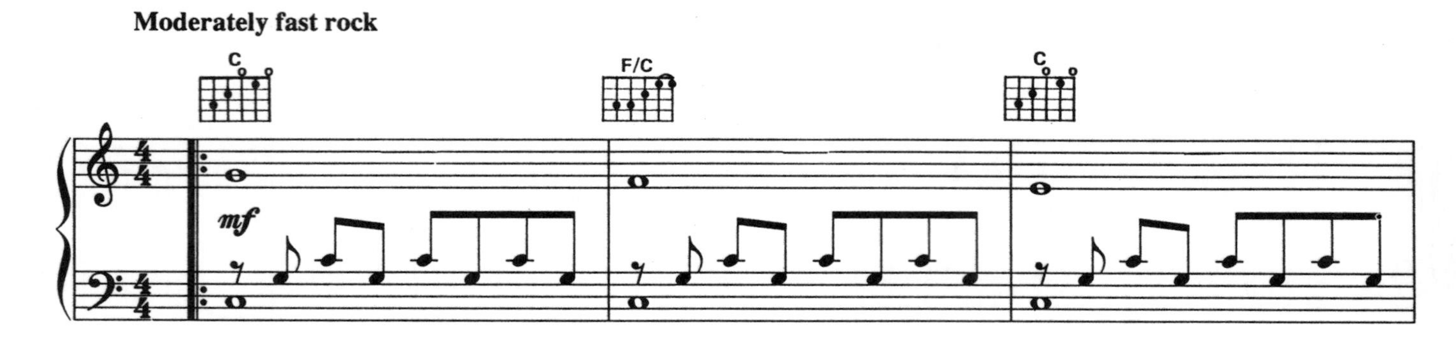


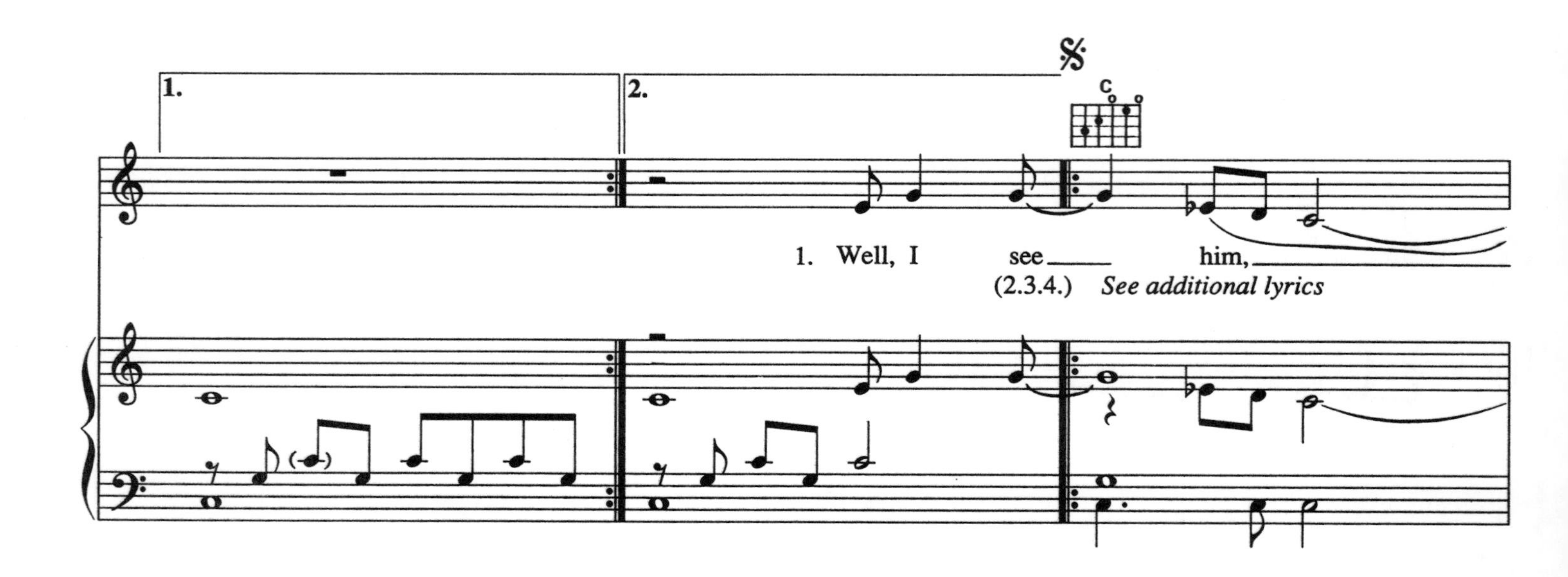

F/C
there's an in- tense - ness
C
in him,
in his eyes.
He
F/C
wants me to be with him,
He
C
wants me with him now.
F
Oh,

G
F
— she just seems to be miss - in'. ___
1.
How could that hap - pen ___ an - y - how? ___
2.3.4.
2. So one day it just
al - most goes a - way. ___
You spend

F
G
F
lots of time a - lone,
some - times you spend
G
F
G
To Coda
years,
and you miss those arms
that used to
3
C
F/C
C
go a - round you.
3
F
G
Am
Night af - ter
3

F
G
Am
night, no ques - tions asked; and
F
G
Am
F
G
who gets the cold wind of it all,
Am
F
G
Am
ev - 'ry - time. Well, it's hard to be civ - il and it's
F
G
Am
F
real hard to be nice, but you did it, my

G
C
F/C
love, —
ev - 'ry time. —
C
F/C
C
D.S. al Coda
3. So
Coda
Repeat and fade
C
F/C
Need
you now, —

2. So how can you say,
"Well, I don't know what love is"?
You have it, and you have no time for it.
You feel completely indifferent.
You feel pushed up against the wall.
And then one day it just almost goes away.

3. So, how can you say,
"Well, I can't see you, not now,
Not tomorrow, not until it's right,
Not until neither of us is
Pushed up against the wall"?
I don't throw the cold winds of it
At you . . . anymore.

4. So today she says,
"Well, I changed my mind,
That's a woman's right, they say."
Well, I'm frightened and I'm lost
And I can't give you up, not now.
I need you now, I'm brokenhearted.
I broke down like a little girl.

# GYPSY

Words and Music by
STEVIE NICKS

Fmaj7
F6
F
to the vel - vet
un - der - ground,
B♭maj7
C
B♭maj7
back to the floor
that I love;
C
F
Fmaj7
to a room
with some lace
F6
F
B♭maj7
and pa - per
flow - ers;
back to the gyp -

C
B♭maj7
C
sy
that I was,
to the gyp-
B♭maj7
C
F
sy
that I
was.
Fmaj7
F6
F
B♭maj7
C
B♭maj7

C
F
Fmaj7
And it all comes down to you.
F6
F
B♭maj7
Well, you know that it does. Well, light - ning strikes,
C
B♭maj7
C
may - be once, may - be twice. Ah,
F
Fmaj7
F6
and it lights up the night.

F
Bbmaj7
C
And you see your gyp - sy.
Bbmaj7
C
Bbmaj7
You see your gyp - sy.
C
F
Fmaj7
F6
F
Dm
To the gyp - sy

C
that re - mains,
fac - es
F
Bb
free - dom with a lit - tle fear,
Dm
I have no fear.
I have on - ly
C
F
love.
And if I was a child,

B♭
and the child was e - nough,
e - nough for me
Dm
to love,
e - nough to
C
love.
F
She is danc - ing
Fmaj7
a - way
F6
from me now.
F
B♭maj7
She was just a wish.

C
B♭maj7
C
She was just a wish.
F
Fmaj7
F6
And a mem-o-ry is all that is left for you now.
F
B♭maj7
C
You see your gyp - sy.
B♭maj7
C
B♭maj7
You see your gyp - sy.

**Vocal Ad Lib**

Lightning strikes, maybe once, maybe twice.
And it all comes down to you.
I still see your bright eyes.
And it all comes down to you.

# THAT'S ENOUGH FOR ME

Words and Music by
LINDSEY BUCKINGHAM

Eb
Yeah.
Yeah.
Yeah.
Yeah.
Bb
F
Bb
Oh,
yeah.
D. C. (lyric 2) al Coda
Coda
F
Bb
And that's e-nough for me.
F
Bb
And that's e-nough for me.

# OVER & OVER

Words and Music by
CHRISTINE McVIE

C
D
G
Don't waste our time.
Tell me now.
C
D
G
C
All you have to do
G
Em
C
is speak out my name,
and I would come run-
D
G
ning an-y-way.
And I said,

Em
G/D
could it be me?
Could it real -
C♯m7-5
C6
ly, real - ly be?
O - ver and o -
G
G/F
C/E
ver.
Could it real - ly, real - ly be?
Cm/E♭
G
C
Don't turn me a - way.

G
Em
C
And don't let me down.
What can I do
D
G
G/F
to keep you a - round?
C/E
Cm/E♭
Repeat and fade
G
O - ver and o - ver.
Repeat and fade
G/F
C/E
Cm/E♭
O - ver and o - ver.
O - ver and o - ver.

# SISTERS OF THE MOON

Words and Music by
STEVIE NICKS

Am
F
black wid-ow spi - der makes more sound than she.
And so I fol - lowed, as friends of - ten do.
(mf)
Am
F
And black moons in those eyes of hers made
I cared not for love nor mon - ey,
Am
more sense to me.
and I think she knew.
Heav - y per - sua -
Well, the peo - ple, they love
F
Am
sion: it was hard to breathe. She was
her, but still they're the most cruel. She

F
dark at the top of the stairs. She called
asked me, "Be my sis - ter, Sis - ter
cresc.
Am(no3rd)
G(no3rd)
3fr.
E(no3rd)
F(no3rd)
to me.
of the Moon."
f
E(no3rd)
F(no3rd) G(no3rd)
3fr.
Am(no3rd)
G(no3rd)
3fr.
E(no3rd)
F(no3rd)
E(no3rd)
F(no3rd) G(no3rd)
3fr.
Am(no3rd)

F
G
x000
Some call her "Sis - ter of the Moon."
Some say il - lu - sions
mf
Am
are her game.
They like - to wrap her in vel - vet.
Does an - y - one know her name?
cresc.
Four times
Am(no3rd) G(no3rd) E(no3rd) F(no3rd) E(no3rd) F(no3rd) G(no3rd) Am(no3rd)
3fr.
f Four times

Am(no3rd)
G(no3rd)
3fr.
E(no3rd)
F(no3rd)
So we make our choic - es when
there is no choice.
We lis-ten to their
voic - es, but ig - nor-ing our own voice.
Repeat and fade
Repeat and fade

# BROWN EYES

Words and Music by
CHRISTINE McVIE

Do — you have to have — me — the
just — an-oth-er li - ar? — Will you
A
way that I want you, — I want you? —
take me all the way, — all the way? —
Bm7
Bm7
Sha la la, — sha la la, — sha la la — la la
G
la la — la la. —
Bm7
Sha la la, — sha la la, —

G
Bm7
G
Bm7
G
— sha la la — la la la la — la la. —
Sha la la, — sha la la, — sha la la — la la la la — la la. —
Sha la la, — sha la la, — sha la la — la la
la la — la la. —
1.
2.
D. S. 𝄋 and fade

# THE CHAIN

Words and Music by
LINDSEY BUCKINGHAM, CHRISTINE McVIE,
STEVIE NICKS, MICK FLEETWOOD and JOHN McVIE

Run in the shad - ows.
A
A7
Bm / D
Am / C
Em (no 3rd)
Damn your love; damn your lies.
Play second time only
Break the si - lence.
A
A7
Bm / D
Am / C
Em (no 3rd)
Damn the dark; damn the light.

Am7
And if you don't love me now, you will
Em
C
nev - er love me a - gain. I can still hear you say - in' you would
D sus4
Am7
nev - er break the chain. And if you don't love me now, you will
Em
C
nev - er love me a - gain. I can still hear you say - in' you would
f

1.
D sus4
Em (no 3rd)
Nev - er break the chain.
nev - er break the chain.
mf
2.
D sus4
Am7
nev - er break the chain. And if you don't love me now, you will
Em
C
nev - er love me a - gain. I can still hear you say - in' you would

Dsus4
Em (no 3rd)
C-5/E
Nev - er break the chain.
nev-er break the chain.
Em (no 3rd)
C-5/E
Em (no 3rd)
C-5/E
Em (no 3rd)
C-5/E
Em (no 3rd)
pp
No chord
Am
C
G6
Em
mf
f
8va
Repeat and fade
Am
C
G6
Em
Chain, keep us to - geth - er. Run in the shad- ows.
(8va)

# ANGEL

Words and Music by
STEVIE NICKS

Medium beat

C
keep pass-in' me by.
D
C
D
You feel good.
G
C
D
G
I said it's fun-ny that you un-der-stood.
C
D
G
C
I knew you would.
When you were
good,

D
you were ver - y, ___ ver - y good. ___
C
D
So I
C
close my eyes soft - ly till I be-come ___
D
that part of the wind ___ that we all long ___ for some - time,
C
yeah, _

D
C
and to those that I love like a
ghost through a fog, like a charmed ho-ur and a haunt-ed song, and the an-
gel of my dreams,
an - gel of my

D
To Coda
C
D
dreams.
He said
you feel good.
G
C
D
G
I said it's funny that you under-stood.
C
D
G
C
I knew you would.
When you were
good,
D
ba - by,
mm,
you were ver-y good.

C
D
C
I still look up when you walk
D
C
in the room. I've the same wide eyes.
D
Now, they tell a sto - ry. I try not to

C
D
reach out.
When you turn a - round,
you say hel - lo.
And we both pre - tend.
No great pre - tend -
er.
So I
D. S. al Coda
Coda
Repeat (vocal ad lib) and fade
Repeat and fade

# THINK ABOUT ME

Words and Music by
CHRISTINE McVIE

Dm
B♭
F
— you; did - n't think it would work — out.
But I knew — we would be to - geth -
Gm7
3fr.
F
er, and I could - n't wait for more. —
C
Dm
B♭
What can they say? — It's not a - gainst — the law. —

F
F
Dm
I don't hold you down.
C
F
F/C
And may - be that's why you're a - round.
Bb
F
But if I'm the one you love,
think a - bout me.
I be - lieve

F
that you real - ly want me.
But it's not
Gm7
3fr.
F
C
eas - y just to give in.
So let your-self go
Dm
B♭
F
and let love be - gin.
Ba - by, once in a while,
Repeat and fade
F
think a - bout me.
Ba -by, once in a while,
Repeat and fade

# NOT THAT FUNNY

Words and Music by
LINDSEY BUCKINGHAM

G(no3rd)
3fr.
F(no3rd)
G
Don't
blame
F
G
F
me,
please,
G
F
G
please,
please.
F
G
F
I did-n't wan-na bleed so.
You're here 'cause I say so.

G
F
G
I didn't wanna be this late, so
F
C
G7
don't make me wait.
C
1.
G7
2.
G7
Well, it's
C
G7
C
Here comes the night - time.
Look-in' for a lit - tle more.

G7
C
G7
Wait-in' on the right time.
C
G7
C
Some-bod-y out-side the door, yeah,
G7
C
G7
uh-huh. It's
Repeat and fade
C
G7
C
G7
not that fun-ny, is it? It's not that fun-ny, is it? It's
Repeat and fade

# I DON'T WANT TO KNOW

Words and Music by
STEVIE NICKS

B
F#
E
F#
B
F#
I don't want to know the rea - sons why love keeps right on a-walk-in' on down
E
F#
B
F#
E
F#
the line.
I don't want to stand 'tween you and love. Hon-ey, I just
B
F#
E
F#
B
E
F#
want you to feel fine.
Fi - nal-ly, ba - by,
Fi - nal-ly, ba - by,
B
E
F#
B
E
F#
the truth has come down now.
the truth has been told.
Take a
Now, you

B
E
F♯
lis - ten to your spir - it.
tell me that I'm cra - zy.
It's cry -
It's noth - in'
in' out loud,
that I did-n't know.
try - in' to be - lieve.
Try - in' to sur - vive.
Oh, you say you love me, but you don't know
you got me
rock-in' and a-reel - in'.
1.
Oh,

B
E
F♯
yeah.
Ah.
2.
Hang -
in' on to you.
Oh,
yeah.
Ah.
I don't want to know the rea -
sons why love keeps right on a - walk - in' on down

E
F♯
B
F♯
E
F♯
the line.
I don't want to stand 'tween you and love. Hon - ey,
B
F♯
E
F♯
B
F♯
E
take a lit - tle time.
I,
F♯
E
F♯
B
F♯
E
F♯
I don't want to
B
F♯
E
F♯
E
F♯
B
E
B
know.

# GOLD DUST WOMAN

Words and Music by
STEVIE NICKS

Bb/D
D(no 3rd)
G
C
Heart-less chal-lenge, pick your path and I'll pray.
D(no 3rd)
G
C
Wake up in the morn - in'. See your sun - rise,
Rock on, an - cient queen. Fol - low those who
(mp)
G
D(no 3rd)
Bb/D
D(no 3rd)
loves to go down.
pale in your shad-ow.

Bb/D
D(no 3rd)
G
C
Lous - y lov - ers pick their prey, but they
Rul - ers make bad lov - ers. You bet - ter put your
G
D(no 3rd)
Bb/D
D(no 3rd)
nev - er cry out loud, cry out.
king - dom up for sale, up for sale.
Bb
G/B
Well, did she make you cry, make you break down,
cresc.
mf
C
D(no 3rd)
shat - ter your il - lu - sions of love? And is it

B♭
G/B
C
o - ver now? Do you know how to pick up the piec-es and go
1.
D(no 3rd)
B♭/D
D(no 3rd)
B♭/D
D(no 3rd)
home?
dim.
2.
D(no 3rd)
home? Well, did she
B♭
G/B
C
make you cry, make you break down, shat-ter your il - lu-sions of love?

D(no 3rd)
Bb
And now tell me, is it o - ver now? Do
G/B
C
you know how to pick up the piec - es and go
D(no 3rd)
Bb-5/D
D(no 3rd)
Bb-5/D
home, and go home, and go
Repeat and fade
D(no 3rd)
Bb-5/D
D(no 3rd)
Bb-5/D
home?
Repeat and fade

# THE LEDGE

Words and Music by
LINDSEY BUCKINGHAM

C(no3rd)
3fr.
F(no3rd)
Do you ev - er won - der? Do you ev - er hate?
Buy an - oth - er fix - ture. Tell an - oth - er lie.
C(no3rd)
3fr.
F(no3rd)
Six feet un - der, some - one who can wait.
Paint an - oth - er pic - ture. See who's sur - prised.
You can
A(no3rd)
D(no3rd)
C(no3rd)
3 fr.
love me, ba - by, but you can't walk out. Some-one ought to, some-one ought to
G(no3rd)
3fr.
A(no3rd)
tell you what it's real-ly all a - bout.
You're nev - er gon- na

G(no3rd)
3fr.
A(no3rd)
make it, ba - by.
Oh,
you're nev - er gon - na
G(no3rd)
3fr.
F(no3rd)
make it ba - by.
Oh,
you're nev - er gon - na
1.
G(no3rd)
3fr.
Tacet
make it babe, make it babe, make it ba - by.
2.
G(no3rd)
3fr.
Tacet
D. C. (instrumental) and fade
make it babe, make it babe, make it ba - by.